CJ Matthews & Kristen Wrig

AND THEN THERE WAS ONE

Illustrated by Marie Nkomo

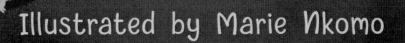

Published by Parker & Co., LLC
P.O. Box 50040
Richmond, VA 23250

ISBN: (paperback): 978-1-952733-42-0
ISBN: (hardback): 978-1-952733-43-7
ISBN: (ebook): 978-1-952733-44-4

To our angel, Karsen Angelica – because you are OUR WHY. You tiptoed into our world silently and stayed only for a moment. But you have left an imprint of your footprints on our hearts and impacted our lives forever.

To the rest of our family: especially Chris (our rock), Kollin - our rainbow baby that restored our family's hope and gave us a joy we never thought imaginable, and to the best parents and grandparents anyone could ask for, Mr. & Mrs. Ronald and Jane Wright (Granny and Papa). We are grateful to have all of you!

We want to thank everyone who has ever prayed, consoled, and supported us in any way along this journey. We dedicate this book to every family who ever endured the loss of a child during pregnancy or otherwise. Stay hopeful and prayerful. To the children who grieve their loss, one day, it will be easier.

Last and certainly not least, we give all glory and praise to our Lord and Savior because only He can turn a TEST into a TESTIMONY!

I was five when my mom experienced a pregnancy loss. I didn't understand everything then, but I knew the baby I wanted so much was not coming home. I took it very hard. My parents and grandparents would find me around the house crying. I had just learned to use the computer, and I could spell, so I was Googling and finding videos too intense for a five-year-old. The videos would make me very sad.

I played soccer and football, but my mind always returned to my sorrow when I wasn't playing. I know my mom was sad, too, but she was worried about me. One day she asked me if I could help another child who had similar feelings of grief; what would I do? What would I give them? Blankets are one of my favorite things, so it was the first thing to come to mind. Like a hug, blankets can give you a sense of comfort and security when you're cold, scared, or even sad, so that's what I picked. She told me that we were going to collect blankets to give to other children.

We had blanket collections and set up a fundraiser on GoFundMe. That year, we donated about 800 blankets to kids in children's hospitals, orphanages, shelters, individuals without houses, etc. I didn't understand why we were doing it then, but it felt good, and I didn't want to stop. My mother explained that my baby sister, Karsen Angelica, was looking down on me and was proud to be my sister. After some time, pride replaced the feelings of sadness. Showing kindness to others made me feel better.

At 14, I realize that a blanket is only a tiny symbol of comfort, but even the smallest act of kindness can build a child's confidence when life gets challenging. Kids need to know that someone cares about what they are going through, as my parents did for me. When I donate a blanket, I want the receiver to know that they matter.

Thank you for supporting my book. By buying this book, you are contributing to making the world a better place for all children.

Kindly,

C. J. Matthews

As a woman who survived the loss of not one baby but two in nine months, I understood the importance of healing for my little boy. I was despondent and barely had the strength to get out of bed each day, but I knew he needed me more than ever during this most critical time in his little life. My husband and I kept him busy with all his physical and educational activities. Still, we realized how important it was for him to experience grieving on a higher level. We didn't have all the answers, but knowing our son, we knew that hands-on was the only way. We started a charitable project in which he could donate blankets to kids who needed comfort. By involving him in every aspect of setting up a charitable project, he took ownership, which ultimately helped him through his grieving process and our own. He had regained his confidence and developed a sense of pride. Witnessing him bringing comfort to others who had experienced loss and other challenging situations, we saw firsthand the benefits and how vital receiving and giving support was to children.

When we experienced the loss of our daughter, we were grasping at straws for the right way to explain it to our son, who was only five years old at the time. The truth of the matter is that there is no right or wrong way to explain, no right or wrong way to grieve, and there is no time limit.

Every situation is different.
Every family is different.
Every individual is different.

Throughout the book, you will notice turtles are hiding in inconspicuous places. During the time we lost our babies, CJ's Papa gave him two tiny turtles. Turtles are symbolic creatures. Because of their long-life span, turtles represent longevity and perseverance; their hard shell symbolizes protection and even healing, all things we need to cope with grief on our journeys from loss. Turtles are celebrated in many cultures for their symbolism, including in Africa, in which they symbolize fertility, something else we wanted. When we decided to publish this book, we wanted to be transparent in sharing our whole experience with readers, the good and the hard times, and especially the uncertain ones to inspire hope and togetherness along your family's process. A lot of thought was put into every page, including the activity pages at the end, which exemplify the five stages of grief to help children identify what they may be feeling and help them find ways to express them.

We hope this book provides an option for families seeking a way to help them grieve because grieving is natural, and it is essential. Keeping grief inside can increase your pain, so we learned to grieve out loud. Our method continues to work for us. Through our work with Blankies 4 My Buddies, we provide comfort for others while keeping our angel's spirit alive. We turned our test into a testimony, and we hope this book inspires you to do the same.

Peace & Blessings,

Through the Blankies 4 My Buddies Foundation, the Matthews' family strives in the fight to improve children's mental health and emotional well-being worldwide, one blanket at a time.

When I was five years old, I was going to be a big brother. My mom was having a baby. I was so excited that it did not matter one bit whether the baby was a boy or girl. I just wanted someone who would look up to me and call me big brother.

For five long years, it was Mom, Dad, and me, just us three, and
I wanted someone new to play with. I was tired of being an only
child.

I would put my ear very close to Mom's belly to see if I could hear breathing. I touched it to feel the baby move.

One day, I felt a really big thump.

Mom said that the baby knew I was there and wanted to let me know by kicking.

I tapped back to see if it would happen again.

"It kicked!" I shouted.

Mom and I laughed and played with the baby until there was no more movement.

"The baby is sleepy now, CJ," Mom said.

At times I would imagine what fun things he and I would do if he were a boy.

Oh, what fun it would be to have a little brother to run around and play football and soccer with, and wrestle, too, I thought.

But if she were a girl, we could have just as much fun. I would teach her how to play all of the cool games that I like to play, like Monopoly and Connect 4. I would teach her how to play football and soccer, too, because girls can do anything boys can do. If she falls and hurts herself, I would help her up and let her know that I would always be here to protect her.

I would say, "I'm your big brother, and I will always take care of you."

Boy OR girl, I was going to be the best big brother ever. I would be a superhero to call their own.

On hot days, we would go to the beach or get wet outside. Papa would make us smoothies to cool us off. He makes the best smoothies ever with bananas, strawberries, grapes, and anything else I want him to add to it.

On cold nights, we would snuggle up in our blankets and watch reruns of all of our favorite television shows.

I loved to help mom around the house and carry in the groceries from the car.

Dad would help, too. He always said, "You have to help your mom, CJ."

But I did not mind because I would do anything for my mom.

I wanted her to get plenty of rest.

One day, my mom was really tired. She said she didn't feel well, so Dad took her to the doctor.

When she came home, she told me that the doctor wanted her to stay in bed until it was time for the baby to come.

A couple of days went by, and Mommy was still sick. Dad took her to the doctor again, but this time, she didn't come back home.

Papa and Granny took me to the hospital to visit her.

I was very sad when it was time to go. I did not want to leave my mom alone.

Dad said, "I will be here, Son, and I will take good care of Mom for you."

When I went to bed that night,

I prayed for her to get well so that she could come home to take care of me and the baby.

I missed her already.

The next day when I saw MOM, she looked really sad.

She said she was fine, but our baby girl had gone to heaven to be with the angels. I was heartbroken.

I did not understand why our baby had to be with the angels when I wanted her right here with me. I had so many plans for us.

I kneeled in the corner and asked God,

"Why did you have to take our baby away?"

But there was no answer.

When MOM came home, everyone was sad, but we spent a lot of time together to prevent ourselves from feeling sad.

We watched movies, played games, and told jokes.

Mom suggested that we celebrate the good memories that we had, like when we felt her kicking and the times when I would read to her.

She told me, "Your baby sister shares these memories, and she will never forget the love that we gave her while she was with us."

She said, "We can continue to show our love for her by doing something in her honor."

We decided to celebrate our baby's life by helping others. We wanted to make her proud to have been a part of our family.

We gave books to sick children to read while they were in the hospital. We collected warm and cozy coats and blankets for kids who were without houses.

We did everything we could to show our baby how much we loved her by showing compassion to others. Helping others feel really good.

God had finally answered my question: Why did you have to take our baby away?

My baby sister was a gift to us. Although losing her was hard, it gave life to our family's new mission to help others. We found our purpose.

And although I really wanted to be a big brother,
I realized that it is OK to be an only child.

There are lots of awesome things that come in only
ONE.

There is only ONE God
no matter what you believe in.

There is only ONE earth.

There is only ONE Christmas Day each year, my favorite holiday!

There can be only ONE President of the United States--at one time.

And there is only ONE me. . .

And I'm fine with that!

What is happening in your life?
Draw a picture to describe what is going on.

You have reached the end of your path, how do
you feel about yourself?
(Circle all that apply to you.)

I AM BRAVE   **I AM STRONG**   **I MATTER**
I AM KIND   **I AM POSITIVE**

Write your own affirmation in the blank
space if you need to.

I AM _____ **I AM** _____

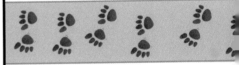

How do I feel?
Circle the face that best describes how you feel.

What do I need?
Place the pebbles that would help you feel better in the bucket.

Draw a line from the pebble to the bucket.

A Friend

A Hug

Your Pet

A Blanket

Love

Sleep

Time Alone

Fill in the blank pebbles if there is nothing here that you need.

Someone Special

When I feel sad, what can I do to feel better?

I CAN_____

I CAN_____

CJ's mom asked him, "If you could do something to prevent other children from feeling sad. **What would you do?**"

CJ chose to give blankets to kids who need comfort and started his charity called Blankies 4 My Buddies.

Draw a picture of yourself helping others.

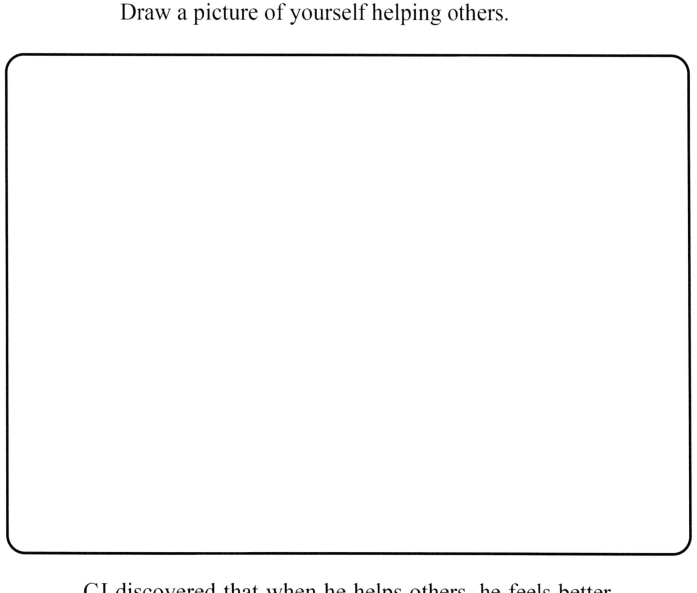

CJ discovered that when he helps others, he feels better.
So when he feels down, he finds a way to serve others.

You can learn all about it at **blankies4mybuddies.org.**

Chris "CJ" Matthews' inspirational story began when his family experienced a loss when he was five years old. His grief sparked an idea: he wanted to do whatever he could to support other kids who might be dealing with similar feelings of sadness. The idea led CJ to create "Blankies 4 My Buddies," which has since grown into a globally recognized organization that brings small tokens of comfort, like cozy blankets, to children dealing with traumatic situations from chronic illnesses to homelessness.

CJ has received numerous awards for his service, including being the 2019 YOU Awards International Community Service Honoree, aired on WSB-TV Atlanta, and he was named a Baskin Robbins Pint-Sized Hero July 2020 for his efforts during the COVID-19 pandemic. CJ is a Giving Tuesday Sparks leader, a youth ambassador in the global generosity movement. And Then There Was One is his first children's book, but he is a published author. His award-winning poem, "I Am Great," appeared in Inklings Book 2019 (Society of Young Inklings, Inc.). The poem was the 1st Place Winner awarded by the South Fulton, GA Council PTA Reflections Program for Literature for the 2016-2017 school year. He also contributed an essay to In Their Own Words: Relevant Essays from Brilliant Young People In The Year 2020.

Kristen Wright Matthews is a wife, mother, and lifelong creative. With over 25 years of experience in public relations and writing, Kristen has spent the past nine years telling her own family's story. After suffering a pregnancy loss when her son CJ was five years old, Kristen's maternal instinct led her in helping him to cope with his grief. The Matthews' created a charitable project called Blankies 4 My Buddies, in which CJ would donate blankets to provide comfort to kids dealing with difficult situations while nurturing his own needs. Since then, CJ and Blankies 4 My Buddies have grown immensely, being featured on such media outlets at Good Morning America, CBS Evening News, and NBC Nightly News with Lester Holt: Kids Edition. She always loved reading children's books and dreamed of a career in children's literature for many years. Kristen has written features and cover stories for various magazines, co-authored and edited a few children's books, and was a co-author of Motherhood Chronicles 2. And Then There Was One is her debut children's book, but it's sure not to be the last.

Made in United States
Orlando, FL
25 August 2022

21563397R00024